Term Service Contract

This contract should be used for the appointment of a supplier for a
period of time to manage and provide a service

An NEC document

June 2005

(with amendments June 2006)

Construction Clients' Board endorsement of NEC3

The Construction Clients' Board (formerly Public Sector Construction
Clients' Forum) recommends that public sector organisations
use the NEC3 contracts when procuring construction. Standardising
use of this comprehensive suite of contracts should help to
deliver efficiencies across the public sector and promote behaviours
in line with the principles of *Achieving Excellence in Construction.*

NEC is a division of Thomas Telford Ltd, which is a wholly owned subsidiary of the Institution of Civil Engineers (ICE), the owner and developer of the NEC.

The NEC is a family of standard contracts, each of which has these characteristics:

- Its use stimulates good management of the relationship between the two parties to the contract and, hence, of the work included in the contract.
- It can be used in a wide variety of commercial situations, for a wide variety of types of work and in any location.
- It is a clear and simple document – using language and a structure which are straightforward and easily understood.

NEC3 Term Service Contract is one of the NEC family and is consistent with all other NEC3 documents. Also available are the Term Service Contract Guidance Notes and the Term Service Contract Flow Charts.

ISBN (complete box set) 978 07277 3675 8
ISBN (this document) 978 07277 3376 4
ISBN (Term Service Contract Guidance Notes) 978 07277 3377 1
ISBN (Term Service Contract Flow Charts) 978 07277 3378 8

First edition June 2005
Reprinted with amendments September 2006
Reprinted 2007, 2009, 2010 (thrice), 2011, 2012 (twice)

Cover photo, Golden Jubilee Bridge, courtesy of City of Westminster

9 8 7 6 5 4

British Library Cataloguing in Publication Data for this publication is available from the British Library.

Typeset by Academic + Technical, Bristol

Printed and bound in Great Britain by Bell & Bain Limited, Glasgow, UK

NTENTS

ACKNOWLEDGEMENTS

The first edition of the NEC3 Term Service Contract was drafted by Institution of Civil Engineers NEC Panel working through its Term Ser Contract Working Group whose members were:

P. A. Baird, BSc, CEng, FICE, M(SA)ICE, MAPM
M. Barnes, BSc(Eng), PhD, FREng, FICE, FCIOB, CCMI, ACIArb, MBCS, FInstCES, FAPM
T. W. Weddell, BSc, CEng, DIC, FICE, FIStructE, ACIArb

The Flow Charts were produced by Ross Hayes with assistance from T Nicholson.

The original NEC was designed and drafted by Dr Martin Barnes then Coopers and Lybrand with the assistance of Professor J. G. Perry then of University of Birmingham, T. W. Weddell then of Travers Morgan Manageme T. H. Nicholson, Consultant to the Institution of Civil Engineers, A. Norm then of the University of Manchester Institute of Science and Technology a P. A. Baird, then Corporate Contracts Consultant, Eskom, South Africa.

The members of the NEC Panel are:

P. Higgins, BSc, CEng, FICE, FCIArb (Chairman)
P. A. Baird, BSc, CEng, FICE, M(SA)ICE, MAPM
M. Barnes, BSc(Eng), PhD, FREng, FICE, FCIOB, CCMI, ACIArb, MBCS, FInstCES, FAPM
A. J. Bates, FRICS, MInstCES
A. J. M. Blackler, BA, LLB(Cantab), MCIArb
P. T. Cousins, BEng(Tech), DipArb, CEng, MICE, MCIArb, MCMI
L. T. Eames, BSc, FRICS, FCIOB
F. Forward, BA(Hons), DipArch, MSc(Const Law), RIBA, FCIArb
Professor J. G. Perry, MEng, PhD, CEng, FICE, MAPM
N. C. Shaw, FCIPS, CEng, MIMechE
T. W. Weddell, BSc, CEng, DIC, FICE, FIStructE, ACIArb

NEC Consultant:

R. A. Gerrard, BSc(Hons), MRICS, FCIArb, FInstCES

Secretariat:

A. Cole, LLB, LLM, BL
J. M. Hawkins, BA(Hons), MSc
F. N. Vernon (Technical Adviser), BSc, CEng, MICE

The strategy for choosing the form of contract starts with a decision between three main Options, one of which must be chosen.

Option A	Priced contract with price list
Option C	Target contract with price list
Option E	Cost reimbursable contract
Note	Options B and D are not used

One of the following dispute resolution Options must be selected to complete the chosen main Option.

Option W1	Dispute resolution procedure (used unless the United Kingdom Housing Grants, Construction and Regeneration Act 1996 applies).
Option W2	Dispute resolution procedure (used in the United Kingdom when the Housing Grants, Construction and Regeneration Act 1996 applies).

The following secondary Options should then be considered. It is not necessary to use any of them. Any combination other than those stated may be used.

Option X1	Price adjustment for inflation (used only with Options A and C)
Option X2	Changes in the law
Option X3	Multiple currencies (used only with Option A)
Option X4	Parent company guarantee
Option X12	Partnering
Option X13	Performance bond
Option X17	Low service damages
Option X18	Limitation of liability
Option X19	Task Order
Option X20	Key Performance Indicators (not used with Option X12)

The following Options dealing with national legislation should be included if required.

Option Y(UK)2	The Housing Grants, Construction and Regeneration Act 1996
Option Y(UK)3	The Contracts (Rights of Third Parties) Act 1999
Option Z	*Additional conditions of contract*
Note	Options X5 to X11 and X14 to X16 are not used.

AMENDMENTS JUNE 2006

The following amendments have been made to the June 2005 edition.

Page	Clause	Line	
7	22.1	2	deleted: ', notifed early warning matters'
19	90.2, Termination Table The *Employer*	4	Procedure column: ', P3' inserted after 'P2'
		4	Amount due column: ', A2' inserted after 'A1'
	90.2, Termination Table The *Contractor*	7	Procedure column: 'P3' replaced with 'P2'
		9	Procedure column: 'P3' replaced with 'P2'
38	X19.8	4	deleted: 'and of notified early warning matters'
39	X20.4	1	'mount' replaced with 'amount'
41	Contract Data Part one, 1. General	3	added before full stop: '(with amendments June 2006)'
42	Contract Data Part one, 8. Risks and insurance	3	deleted: 'The minimum amount of cover for loss of or damage to Plant and Materials provided by the *Employer* is ...'
43	Contract Data Part one, 1. Optional statements	1	deleted: 'If there are additional compensation events' and following 4 lines

AMENDMENTS JUNE 2006

nec®3 Term Service Contract

ꓱRE CLAUSES

General

<table>
<tr><td>Actions</td><td>10</td><td></td></tr>
<tr><td></td><td>10.1</td><td>The Employer, the Contractor and the Service Manager shall act as stated in this contract and in a spirit of mutual trust and co-operation.</td></tr>
<tr><td>Identified and defined terms</td><td>11</td><td></td></tr>
<tr><td></td><td>11.1</td><td>In these conditions of contract, terms identified in the Contract Data are in italics and defined terms have capital initials.</td></tr>
</table>

11.2   (1) The Accepted Plan is the plan identified in the Contract Data or is the latest plan accepted by the *Service Manager*. The latest plan accepted by the *Service Manager* supersedes previous Accepted Plans.

(2) Affected Property is property of the *Employer* or Others which is affected by the work of the *Contractor* or used by the *Contractor* in Providing the Service and which is identified in the Contract Data.

(3) The Contract Date is the date when this contract came into existence.

(4) A Defect is

- a part of the *service* which is not provided in accordance with the Service Information or
- a part of the *service* which is not in accordance with the applicable law or the Accepted Plan.

(5) Defined Cost is payments by the *Contractor* in Providing the Service for

- people who are employed by the *Contractor*,
- Plant and Materials,
- work subcontracted by the *Contractor* and
- Equipment,

less Disallowed Cost.

The amount for Equipment includes amounts paid for hired Equipment and an amount for the use of Equipment owned by the *Contractor* which is the amount the *Contractor* would have paid if the Equipment had been hired.

(6) Disallowed Cost is cost which the *Service Manager* decides

- is not justified by the *Contractor*'s accounts and records,
- should not have been paid to a Subcontractor or supplier in accordance with his contract,
- was incurred only because the *Contractor* did not
  - follow an acceptance or procurement procedure stated in the Service Information or
  - give an early warning which this contract required him to give

core clauses

main option clauses

secondary option clauses

contract data

and the cost of

- Plant and Materials not used to Provide the Service (after allow for reasonable wastage) unless resulting from a change to the Serv Information,
- resources not used to Provide the Service (after allowing for reasona availability and utilisation) or not taken away when the *Service Mana* requested,
- events for which this contract requires the *Contractor* to insure and
- preparation for and conduct of an adjudication or proceedings of tribunal

and amounts paid to the *Contractor* by insurers.

(7) Equipment is items provided by the *Contractor* and used by him to Prov the Service and which the Service Information does not require him to inclu in the Affected Property.

(8) The Fee is the sum of the amounts calculated by applying the *subc tracted fee percentage* to the Defined Cost of subcontracted work and *direct fee percentage* to the Defined Cost of other work.

(9) Others are people or organisations who are not the *Employer,* the *Serv Manager*, the *Adjudicator*, the *Contractor* or any employee, Subcontractor supplier of the *Contractor.*

(10) The Parties are the *Employer* and the *Contractor.*

(11) Plant and Materials are items intended to be included in the Affect Property.

(12) The Price List is the *price list* unless later changed in accordance w this contract.

(13) To Provide the Service means to do the work necessary to provide t *service* in accordance with this contract and all incidental work, services a actions which this contract requires.

(14) The Risk Register is a register of the risks which are listed in t Contract Data and the risks which the *Service Manager* or the *Contractor* h notified as an early warning matter. It includes a description of the risk and description of the actions which are to be taken to avoid or reduce the risk.

(15) Service Information is information which either

- specifies and describes the *service* or
- states any constraints on how the *Contractor* Provides the Service

and is either

- in the documents which the Contract Data states it is in or
- in an instruction given in accordance with this contract.

(16) A Subcontractor is a person or organisation who has a contract with t *Contractor* to

- provide a part of the *service* or
- supply Plant and Materials which the person or organisation has who or partly designed specifically for the *service.*

Interpretation and the law **12**

12.1   In this contract, except where the context shows otherwise, words in t singular also mean in the plural and the other way round and words in t masculine also mean in the feminine and neuter.

12.2	This contract is governed by the *law of the contract*.
12.3	No change to this contract, unless provided for by the *conditions of contract*, has effect unless it has been agreed, confirmed in writing and signed by the *Parties*.
12.4	This contract is the entire agreement between the *Parties*.

Communications 13

13.1	Each instruction, certificate, submission, proposal, record, acceptance, notification, reply and other communication which this contract requires is communicated in a form which can be read, copied and recorded. Writing is in the *language of this contract*.
13.2	A communication has effect when it is received at the last address notified by the recipient for receiving communications or, if none is notified, at the address of the recipient stated in the Contract Data.
13.3	If this contract requires the *Service Manager* or the *Contractor* to reply to a communication, unless otherwise stated in this contract, he replies within the *period for reply*.
13.4	The *Service Manager* replies to a communication submitted or resubmitted to him by the *Contractor* for acceptance. If his reply is not acceptance, the *Service Manager* states his reasons and the *Contractor* resubmits the communication within the *period for reply* taking account of these reasons. A reason for withholding acceptance is that more information is needed in order to assess the *Contractor*'s submission fully.
13.5	The *Service Manager* may extend the *period for reply* to a communication if the *Service Manager* and the *Contractor* agree to the extension before the reply is due. The *Service Manager* notifies the *Contractor* of the extension which has been agreed.
13.6	The *Service Manager* issues his certificates to the *Employer* and the *Contractor*.
13.7	A notification which this contract requires is communicated separately from other communications.
13.8	The *Service Manager* may withhold acceptance of a submission by the *Contractor*. Withholding acceptance for a reason stated in this contract is not a compensation event.

The *Service Manager* 14

14.1	The *Service Manager*'s acceptance of a communication from the *Contractor* or of his work does not change the *Contractor*'s responsibility to Provide the Service or his liability for his plan or his design.
14.2	The *Service Manager*, after notifying the *Contractor*, may delegate any of his actions and may cancel any delegation. A reference to an action of the *Service Manager* in this contract includes an action by his delegate.
14.3	The *Service Manager* may give an instruction to the *Contractor* which changes the Service Information.
14.4	The *Employer* may replace the *Service Manager* after he has notified the *Contractor* of the name of the replacement.

***Employer* provides right of access and things 15**

15.1	The *Employer* provides the right of access for the *Contractor* to Affected Property as necessary for the work in this contract subject to any constraints stated in the Service Information.
15.2	The *Employer* provides things which he is to provide as stated in the Service Information.

core clauses

main option clauses

secondary option clauses

contract data

Early warning **16**

16.1   The *Contractor* and the *Service Manager* give an early warning by notifying t
other as soon as either becomes aware of any matter which could

- increase the total of the Prices,
- interfere with the timing of the *service* or
- impair the effectiveness of the *service*.

The *Contractor* may give an early warning by notifying the *Service Manager*
any other matter which could increase his total cost. The *Service Manag*
enters early warning matters in the Risk Register. Early warning of a mat'
for which a compensation event has previously been notified is not required.

16.2   Either the *Service Manager* or the *Contractor* may instruct the other to atte
a risk reduction meeting. Each may instruct other people to attend if the otl
agrees.

16.3   At a risk reduction meeting, those who attend co-operate in

- making and considering proposals for how the effect of the register
risks can be avoided or reduced,
- seeking solutions that will bring advantage to all those who will
affected,
- deciding on the actions which will be taken and who, in accordance w
this contract, will take them and
- deciding which risks have now been avoided or have passed and can
removed from the Risk Register.

16.4   The *Service Manager* revises the Risk Register to record the decisions made
each risk reduction meeting and issues the revised Risk Register to t
Contractor. If a decision needs a change to the Service Information, the *Servi*
Manager instructs the change at the same time as he issues the revised Ri
Register.

Ambiguities and **17**
inconsistencies 17.1   The *Service Manager* or the *Contractor* notifies the other as soon as eith
becomes aware of an ambiguity or inconsistency in or between the documen
which are part of this contract. The *Service Manager* gives an instructi
resolving the ambiguity or inconsistency.

Illegal and impossible **18**
requirements 18.1   The *Contractor* notifies the *Service Manager* as soon as he considers that t
Service Information requires him to do anything which is illegal or impossib
If the *Service Manager* agrees, he gives an instruction to change the Servi
Information appropriately.

The *Contractor*'s main responsibilities

Providing the Service **20**

20.1 The *Contractor* Provides the Service in accordance with the Service Information.

20.2 In Providing the Service, the *Contractor* minimises the interference caused to the Affected Property and the activities taking place in it.

The *Contractor*'s plan **21**

21.1 If a plan is not identified in the Contract Data, the *Contractor* submits a first plan to the *Service Manager* for acceptance within the period stated in the Contract Data.

21.2 The *Contractor* shows on each plan which he submits for acceptance

- the *starting date* and the end of the *service period*,
- the order and timing of the work of the *Employer* and Others as last agreed with them by the *Contractor* or, if not so agreed, as stated in the Service Information,
- provisions for

  - time risk allowances,
  - health and safety requirements and
  - the procedures set out in this contract,

- the dates when, in order to Provide the Service in accordance with his plan, the *Contractor* will need

  - access to the Affected Property as stated in the Service Information,
  - acceptances,
  - Plant and Materials, equipment and other things to be provided by the *Employer* and
  - information from Others,

- for each operation, a statement of how the *Contractor* plans to do the work identifying the principal Equipment and other resources which he plans to use and
- other information which the Service Information requires the *Contractor* to show on a plan submitted for acceptance.

21.3 Within two weeks of the *Contractor* submitting a plan to him for acceptance, the *Service Manager* either accepts the plan or notifies the *Contractor* of his reasons for not accepting it. A reason for not accepting a plan is that

- the *Contractor*'s plans which it shows are not practicable,
- it does not show the information which this contract requires,
- it does not represent the *Contractor*'s plans realistically or
- it does not comply with the Service Information.

Revising the *Contractor*'s plan **22**

22.1 The *Contractor* submits a revised plan to the *Service Manager* for acceptance showing the effects of implemented compensation events and other changes. It is submitted

- within the *period for reply* after the *Service Manager* has instructed him to and
- when the *Contractor* chooses to.

core clauses

main option clauses

secondary option clauses

contract data

Design of Equipment 23

23.1 The *Contractor* submits particulars of the design of an item of Equipment the *Service Manager* for acceptance if the *Service Manager* instructs him to reason for not accepting is that the design of the item will not allow Contractor to Provide the Service in accordance with

- the Service Information,
- the Accepted Plan or
- the applicable law.

People 24

24.1 The *Contractor* either employs each key person named to do the job stated the Contract Data or employs a replacement person who has been accept by the *Service Manager*. The *Contractor* submits the name, relevant qu fications and experience of a proposed replacement person to the *Serv Manager* for acceptance. A reason for not accepting the person is that relevant qualifications and experience are not as good as those of the pers who is to be replaced.

24.2 The *Service Manager* may, having stated his reasons, instruct the *Contrac* to remove an employee. The *Contractor* then arranges that, after one day, t employee has no further connection with the work included in this contract.

Working with the *Employer* 25
and Others 25.1 The *Contractor* co-operates with Others in obtaining and providing informati which they need in connection with the *service*. He co-operates with Others a shares the Affected Property with them as stated in the Service Information.

25.2 The *Employer* and the *Contractor* provide facilities and other things as stat in the Service Information. Any cost incurred by the *Employer* as a result the *Contractor* not providing the facilities and other things he is to provide assessed by the *Service Manager* and paid by the *Contractor*.

Subcontracting 26

26.1 If the *Contractor* subcontracts work, he is responsible for Providing the Serv as if he had not subcontracted. This contract applies as if a *Subcontracto* employees and equipment were the *Contractor*'s.

26.2 The *Contractor* submits the name of each proposed Subcontractor to t *Service Manager* for acceptance. A reason for not accepting the Subcontrac is that his appointment will not allow the *Contractor* to Provide the Servic The *Contractor* does not appoint a proposed Subcontractor until the *Serv Manager* has accepted him.

26.3 The *Contractor* submits the proposed conditions of contract for each subcc tract to the *Service Manager* for acceptance unless

- an NEC contract is proposed or
- the *Service Manager* has agreed that no submission is required.

The *Contractor* does not appoint a Subcontractor on the proposed subcontra conditions submitted until the *Service Manager* has accepted them. A reas for not accepting them is that

- they will not allow the *Contractor* to Provide the Service or
- they do not include a statement that the parties to the subcontract sh act in a spirit of mutual trust and co-operation.

Other responsibilities 27

27.1 The *Contractor* obtains approval from Others where necessary.

27.2 The *Contractor* provides access to work being done and to Plant and Materia being stored for this contract for the *Service Manager* and Others notified him by the *Service Manager*.

27.3 The *Contractor* obeys an instruction which is in accordance with this contra and is given to him by the *Service Manager*.

27.4 The *Contractor* acts in accordance with the health and safety requiremen stated in the Service Information.

Time

Starting and the **30**
service period 30.1 The *Contractor* does not start work until the *starting date* and Provides the Service throughout the *service period.*

Access **31**
31.1 The *Employer* allows the *Contractor* access to the Affected Property as shown on the Accepted Plan.

Instructions to stop or not **32**
to start work 32.1 The *Service Manager* may instruct the *Contractor* to stop or not to start any work and may later instruct him that he may re-start or start it.

4 Testing and Defects

Tests and inspections **40**

40.1 The subclauses in this clause only apply to tests and inspections required the Service Information or the applicable law.

40.2 The *Contractor* and the *Employer* provide materials, facilities and samples tests and inspections as stated in the Service Information.

40.3 The *Contractor* and the *Service Manager* each notifies the other of each of tests and inspections before it starts and afterwards notifies the other of results. The *Contractor* notifies the *Service Manager* in time for a test inspection to be arranged and done before doing work which would obstr the test or inspection. The *Service Manager* may watch any test done by t *Contractor*.

40.4 If a test or inspection shows that any work has a Defect, the *Contract* repeats the work if possible and the test or inspection is repeated.

40.5 The *Service Manager* does his tests and inspections without causing unnece sary delay to the work.

40.6 The *Service Manager* assesses the cost incurred by the *Employer* in repeati a test or inspection after a Defect is found. The *Contractor* pays the amou assessed.

Testing and inspection **41**
before delivery 41.1 The *Contractor* does not deliver those Plant and Materials which the Servi Information states are to be tested or inspected before delivery until t *Service Manager* has notified the *Contractor* that they have passed the test inspection.

Correcting Defects **42**

42.1 The *Contractor* corrects Defects within a time which minimises the adver effect on the *Employer* or Others. If the *Contractor* does not correct a Defe within the time required by this contract, the *Service Manager* assesses t cost to the *Employer* of having the Defect corrected by other people and t *Contractor* pays this amount.

42.2 The *Service Manager* arranges for the *Employer* to allow the *Contractor* acce if it is needed for correcting a Defect.

Accepting Defects **43**

43.1 The *Contractor* and the *Service Manager* may each propose to the other th the Service Information should be changed so that a Defect does not have be corrected. If the *Contractor* and the *Service Manager* are prepared consider the change, the *Contractor* submits a quotation for reduced Prices the *Service Manager* for acceptance. If the *Service Manager* accepts t quotation, he gives an instruction to change the Service Information and t Prices accordingly.

Payment

ssessing the amount due 50

50.1   The *Service Manager* assesses the amount due at each assessment date. The first assessment date is decided by the *Service Manager* to suit the procedures of the Parties and is not later than the *assessment interval* after the *starting date*. Later assessment dates occur at the end of each *assessment interval* until four weeks after the end of the *service period*.

50.2   The amount due is

- the Price for Services Provided to Date,
- plus other amounts to be paid to the *Contractor*,
- less amounts to be paid by or retained from the *Contractor*.

Any tax which the law requires the *Employer* to pay to the *Contractor* is included in the amount due.

50.3   If no plan is identified in the Contract Data, one quarter of the Price for Services Provided to Date is retained in assessments of the amount due until the *Contractor* has submitted a first plan to the *Service Manager* for acceptance showing the information which this contract requires.

50.4   In assessing the amount due, the *Service Manager* considers any application for payment the *Contractor* has submitted on or before the assessment date. The *Service Manager* gives the *Contractor* details of how the amount due has been assessed.

50.5   The *Service Manager* corrects any wrongly assessed amount due in a later payment certificate.

Payment 51

51.1   The *Service Manager* certifies a payment within one week of each assessment date. The first payment is the amount due. Other payments are the change in the amount due since the last payment certificate. A payment is made by the *Contractor* to the *Employer* if the change reduces the amount due. Other payments are made by the *Employer* to the *Contractor*. Payments are in the *currency of this contract* unless otherwise stated in this contract.

51.2   Each certified payment is made within three weeks of the assessment date or, if a different period is stated in the Contract Data, within the period stated. If a certified payment is late, or if a payment is late because the *Service Manager* does not issue a certificate which he should issue, interest is paid on the late payment. Interest is assessed from the date by which the late payment should have been made until the date when the late payment is made, and is included in the first assessment after the late payment is made.

51.3   If an amount due is corrected in a later certificate either

- by the *Service Manager* in relation to a mistake or a compensation event or
- following a decision of the *Adjudicator* or the *tribunal*,

interest on the correcting amount is paid. Interest is assessed from the date when the incorrect amount was certified until the date when the correcting amount is certified and is included in the assessment which includes the correcting amount.

51.4   Interest is calculated on a daily basis at the *interest rate* and is compounded annually.

Defined Cost 52

52.1   All the *Contractor*'s costs which are not included in the Defined Cost are treated as included in the Fee. Amounts included in Defined Cost are at open market or competitively tendered prices with deductions for all discounts, rebates and taxes which can be recovered.

core clauses

main option clauses

secondary option clauses

contract data

6 Compensation events

Compensation events 60

60.1 The following are compensation events.

(1) The *Service Manager* gives an instruction changing the Service Information except

- a change made in order to accept a Defect or
- a change to the Service Information provided by the *Contractor* for plan which is made either at his request or to comply with other Service Information provided by the *Employer*.

(2) The *Employer* does not provide the right of access to the Affected Property in accordance with the Accepted Plan.

(3) The *Employer* does not provide something which he is to provide as stated in the Service Information in accordance with the Accepted Plan.

(4) The *Service Manager* gives an instruction to stop or not to start any work.

(5) The *Employer* or Others do not work in accordance with the Accepted Plan or within the conditions stated in the Service Information.

(6) The *Service Manager* does not reply to a communication from the *Contractor* within the period required by this contract.

(7) The *Service Manager* changes a decision which he has previously communicated to the *Contractor*.

(8) The *Service Manager* withholds an acceptance (other than acceptance of a quotation for not correcting a Defect) for a reason not stated in the contract.

(9) A test or inspection done by the *Service Manager* causes unnecessary delay.

(10) A change to the Affected Property other than a change as a result of Providing the Service.

(11) The *Employer* does not provide materials, facilities and samples for tests and inspections as stated in the Service Information.

(12) An event which is an *Employer*'s risk in this contract.

(13) The *Service Manager* notifies a correction to an assumption which has stated about a compensation event.

(14) A breach of contract by the *Employer* which is not one of the other compensation events in this contract.

Notifying compensation 61
events 61.1 For compensation events which arise from the *Service Manager* giving instruction or changing an earlier decision, the *Service Manager* notifies the *Contractor* of the compensation event at the time of giving the instruction changing the earlier decision. He also instructs the *Contractor* to submit quotations, unless the event arises from a fault of the *Contractor* or quotations have already been submitted. The *Contractor* puts the instruction changed decision into effect.

61.2 The *Service Manager* may instruct the *Contractor* to submit quotations for proposed instruction or a proposed changed decision. The *Contractor* does not put a proposed instruction or a proposed changed decision into effect.

61.3   The *Contractor* notifies the *Service Manager* of an event which has happened or which he expects to happen as a compensation event if

- the *Contractor* believes that the event is a compensation event and
- the *Service Manager* has not notified the event to the *Contractor*.

If the *Contractor* does not notify a compensation event within eight weeks of becoming aware of the event, he is not entitled to a change in the Prices unless the *Service Manager* should have notified the event to the *Contractor* but did not.

61.4   If the *Service Manager* decides that an event notified by the *Contractor*

- arises from a fault of the *Contractor*,
- has not happened and is not expected to happen,
- has no effect upon Defined Cost or
- is not one of the compensation events stated in this contract

he notifies the *Contractor* of his decision that the Prices are not to be changed.

If the *Service Manager* decides otherwise, he notifies the *Contractor* accordingly and instructs him to submit quotations.

If the *Service Manager* does not notify his decision to the *Contractor* within either

- one week of the *Contractor*'s notification or
- a longer period to which the *Contractor* has agreed,

the *Contractor* may notify the *Service Manager* to this effect. A failure by the *Service Manager* to reply within two weeks of this notification is treated as acceptance by the *Service Manager* that the event is a compensation event and an instruction to submit quotations.

61.5   If the *Service Manager* decides that the *Contractor* did not give an early warning of the event which an experienced contractor could have given, he notifies this decision to the *Contractor* when he instructs him to submit quotations.

61.6   If the *Service Manager* decides that the effects of a compensation event are too uncertain to be forecast reasonably, he states assumptions about the event in his instruction to the *Contractor* to submit quotations. Assessment of the event is based on these assumptions. If any of them is later found to have been wrong, the *Service Manager* notifies a correction.

61.7   A compensation event is not notified after the end of the *service period*.

Quotations for **62**
compensation events 62.1   After discussing with the *Contractor* different ways of dealing with the compensation event which are practicable, the *Service Manager* may instruct the *Contractor* to submit alternative quotations. The *Contractor* submits the required quotations to the *Service Manager* and may submit quotations for other methods of dealing with the compensation event which he considers practicable.

62.2   Quotations for compensation events comprise proposed changes to the Prices assessed by the *Contractor*. The *Contractor* submits details of his assessment with each quotation. If the plan for remaining work is altered by the compensation event, the *Contractor* includes the alterations to the Accepted Plan in his quotation.

62.3 The *Contractor* submits quotations within three weeks of being instructed
do so by the *Service Manager.* The *Service Manager* replies within two wee
of the submission. His reply is

- an instruction to submit a revised quotation,
- an acceptance of a quotation,
- a notification that a proposed instruction will not be given or a propos
changed decision will not be made or
- a notification that he will be making his own assessment.

62.4 The *Service Manager* instructs the *Contractor* to submit a revised quotati
only after explaining his reasons for doing so to the *Contractor.* The *Contrac*
submits the revised quotation within three weeks of being instructed to do s

62.5 The *Service Manager* extends the time allowed for

- the *Contractor* to submit quotations for a compensation event and
- the *Service Manager* to reply to a quotation

if the *Service Manager* and the *Contractor* agree to the extension before t
submission or reply is due. The *Service Manager* notifies the extension th
has been agreed to the *Contractor.*

62.6 If the *Service Manager* does not reply to a quotation within the time allowe
the *Contractor* may notify the *Service Manager* to this effect. If the *Contrac*
submitted more than one quotation for the compensation event, he states
his notification which quotation he proposes is to be accepted. If the *Servi*
Manager does not reply to the notification within two weeks, and unless t
quotation is for a proposed instruction or a proposed changed decisic
the *Contractor*'s notification is treated as acceptance of the quotation by t
Service Manager.

Assessing compensation 63
events 63.1 For a compensation event which only affects the quantities of work shown
the Price List, the change to the Prices is assessed by multiplying t
changed quantities of work by the appropriate rates in the Price List.

63.2 For other compensation events, the changes to the Prices are assessed
the effect of the compensation event upon

- the actual Defined Cost of the work already done,
- the forecast Defined Cost of the work not yet done and
- the resulting Fee.

The date when the *Service Manager* instructed or should have instructed t
Contractor to submit quotations divides the work already done from the wo
not yet done.

Effects on the Defined Cost are assessed separately for

- people who are employed by the *Contractor,*
- Plant and Materials,
- work subcontracted by the *Contractor* and
- Equipment.

The *Contractor* shows how each of these effects is built up in each quotatic
for a compensation event.

63.3 If the *Service Manager* and the *Contractor* agree, rates and Prices in the Pri
List may be used as a basis for assessment instead of Defined Cost and t
resulting Fee.

63.4 If the effect of a compensation event is to reduce the total Defined Cost, t
Prices are not reduced except as stated in this contract.

63.5 The rights of the *Employer* and the *Contractor* to changes to the Prices a
their only rights in respect of a compensation event.

63.6 If the *Service Manager* has notified the *Contractor* of his decision that the *Contractor* did not give an early warning of a compensation event which an experienced contractor could have given, the event is assessed as if the *Contractor* had given early warning.

63.7 Assessment of the effect of a compensation event includes risk allowances for cost for matters which have a significant chance of occurring and are at the *Contractor*'s risk under this contract.

63.8 Assessments are based upon the assumptions that the *Contractor* reacts competently and promptly to the compensation event, that any Defined Cost due to the event is reasonably incurred and that the Accepted Plan can be changed.

63.9 A compensation event which is an instruction to change the Service Information in order to resolve an ambiguity or inconsistency is assessed as if the Prices were for the interpretation most favourable to the Party which did not provide the Service Information.

The *Service Manager*'s **64**
assessments 64.1 The *Service Manager* assesses a compensation event

- if the *Contractor* has not submitted a quotation and details of his assessment within the time allowed,
- if the *Service Manager* decides that the *Contractor* has not assessed the compensation event correctly in a quotation and he does not instruct the *Contractor* to submit a revised quotation,
- if, when the *Contractor* submits quotations for a compensation event, he has not submitted a plan or alterations to a plan which this contract requires him to submit or
- if, when the *Contractor* submits quotations for a compensation event, the *Service Manager* has not accepted the *Contractor*'s latest plan for one of the reasons stated in this contract.

64.2 The *Service Manager* notifies the *Contractor* of his assessment of a compensation event and gives him details of it within the period allowed for the *Contractor*'s submission of his quotation for the same event. This period starts when the need for the *Service Manager*'s assessment becomes apparent.

64.3 If the *Service Manager* does not assess a compensation event within the time allowed, the *Contractor* may notify the *Service Manager* to this effect. If the *Contractor* submitted more than one quotation for the compensation event, he states in his notification which quotation he proposes is to be accepted. If the *Service Manager* does not reply within two weeks of this notification the notification is treated as acceptance of the *Contractor*'s quotation by the *Service Manager*.

Implementing **65**
compensation events 65.1 A compensation event is implemented when

- the *Service Manager* notifies his acceptance of the *Contractor*'s quotation,
- the *Service Manager* notifies the *Contractor* of his own assessment or
- a *Contractor*'s quotation is treated as having been accepted by the *Service Manager*.

65.2 The assessment of a compensation event is not revised if a forecast upon which it is based is shown by later recorded information to have been wrong.

core clauses

main option clauses

secondary option clauses

contract data

7 Use of equipment, Plant and Materials

The Parties' use of
equipment, Plant and
Materials

70

70.1 The *Contractor* has the right to use equipment, Plant and Materials provided by the *Employer* only to Provide the Service.

70.2 At the end of the *service period* the *Contractor*

- returns to the *Employer*, equipment and surplus Plant and Materials provided by the *Employer*,
- provides items of Equipment for the *Employer*'s use as stated in the Service Information and
- provides information and other things as stated in the Service Information

Risks and insurance

Employer's risks **80**

80.1 The following are *Employer*'s risks.

- Claims, proceedings, compensation and costs payable which are due to

  - the unavoidable result of the *service* or of Providing the Service,
  - negligence, breach of statutory duty or interference with any legal right by the *Employer* or by any person employed by or contracted to him except the *Contractor* or
  - a fault of the *Employer* or a fault in his design.

- Loss of or damage to Plant and Materials supplied to the *Contractor* by the *Employer*, or by Others on the *Employer*'s behalf, until the *Contractor* has received and accepted them.
- Loss of or damage to the Affected Property, Plant and Materials due to

  - war, civil war, rebellion, revolution, insurrection, military or usurped power,
  - strikes, riots and civil commotion not confined to the *Contractor*'s employees or
  - radioactive contamination.

- Loss of or wear or damage to any Equipment, Plant and Materials retained by the *Employer* after a termination, except loss, wear or damage due to the activities of the *Contractor* after the termination.
- Additional *Employer*'s risks stated in the Contract Data.

The *Contractor*'s risks **81**

81.1 From the *starting date* until the end of the *service period*, the risks which are not carried by the *Employer* are carried by the *Contractor*.

Indemnity **82**

82.1 Each Party indemnifies the other against claims, proceedings, compensation and costs due to an event which is at his risk.

82.2 The liability of each Party to indemnify the other is reduced if events at the other Party's risk contributed to the claims, proceedings, compensation and costs. The reduction is in proportion to the extent that events which were at the other Party's risk contributed, taking into account each Party's responsibilities under this contract.

Insurance cover **83**

83.1 The *Contractor* provides the insurances stated in the Insurance Table except any insurance which the *Employer* is to provide as stated in the Contract Data. The *Contractor* provides additional insurances as stated in the Contract Data.

83.2 The insurances are in the joint names of the Parties and provide cover for events which are at the *Contractor*'s risk from the *starting date* until the end of the *service period* or a termination certificate has been issued.

core clauses

main option clauses

secondary option clauses

contract data

© copyright nec 2005

INSURANCE TABLE

Insurance against	Minimum amount of cover or minimum limit of indemnity
Loss of or damage caused by the *Contractor* to the *Employer*'s property	The amount stated in the Contract Data
Loss of or damage to Plant and Materials	The replacement cost, including the amount stated in the Contract Data for the replacement of any Plant and Materials provided by the *Employer*
Loss of or damage to Equipment	The replacement cost
The *Contractor*'s liability for loss of or damage to property (except the *Employer*'s property, Plant and Materials and Equipment) and liability for bodily injury to or death of a person (not an employee of the *Contractor*) arising from or in connection with the *Contractor*'s Providing the Service	The amount stated in the Contract Data for any one event with cross liability so that the insurance applies to the Parties separately
Liability for death of or bodily injury to employees of the *Contractor* arising out of and in the course of their employment in connection with this contract	The greater of the amount required by the applicable law and the amount stated in the Contract Data for any one event

Insurance policies 84

84.1 Before the *starting date* and on each renewal of the insurance policy, t Contractor submits to the *Service Manager* for acceptance certificates whi state that the insurance required by this contract is in force. The certificat are signed by the *Contractor*'s insurer or insurance broker. A reason for r accepting the certificates is that they do not comply with this contract.

84.2 Insurance policies include a waiver by the insurers of their subrogation righ against directors and other employees of every insured except where there fraud.

84.3 The Parties comply with the terms and conditions of the insurance policies.

84.4 Any amount not recovered from an insurer is borne by the *Employer* for even which are at his risk and by the *Contractor* for events which are at his risk.

If the *Contractor* does not insure 85

85.1 The *Employer* may insure a risk which this contract requires the *Contractor* insure if the *Contractor* does not submit a required certificate. The cost of th insurance to the *Employer* is paid by the *Contractor*.

Insurance by the *Employer* 86

86.1 The *Service Manager* submits policies and certificates for insurances provid by the *Employer* to the *Contractor* for acceptance before the *starting date* a afterwards as the *Contractor* instructs. The *Contractor* accepts the polici and certificates if they comply with this contract.

86.2 The *Contractor*'s acceptance of an insurance policy or certificate provided the *Employer* does not change the responsibility of the *Employer* to provi the insurances stated in the Contract Data.

86.3 The *Contractor* may insure a risk which this contract requires the *Employer* insure if the *Employer* does not submit a required policy or certificate. T cost of this insurance to the *Contractor* is paid by the *Employer*.

Termination

Termination 90

90.1 If either Party wishes to terminate the *Contractor*'s obligation to Provide the Service, he notifies the *Service Manager* and the other Party giving details of his reason for terminating. The *Service Manager* issues a termination certificate to both Parties promptly if the reason complies with this contract.

90.2 The *Contractor* may terminate only for a reason identified in the Termination Table. The *Employer* may terminate for any reason. The procedures followed and the amounts due on termination are in accordance with the Termination Table.

TERMINATION TABLE

Terminating Party	Reason	Procedure	Amount due
The *Employer*	A reason other than R1–R21	P1, P2 and P4	A1, A2 and A4
	R1–R15 or R18	P1, P2, P3 and P4	A1, A2 and A3
	R17 or R20	P1 and P4	A1 and A2
	R21	P1, P3 and P4	A1 and A2
The *Contractor*	R1–R10, R16 or R19	P1, P2 and P4	A1, A2 and A4
	R17 or R20	P1, P2 and P4	A1 and A2

90.3 The procedures for termination are implemented immediately after the *Service Manager* has issued a termination certificate.

90.4 Within thirteen weeks of termination, the *Service Manager* certifies a final payment to or from the *Contractor* which is the *Service Manager*'s assessment of the amount due on termination less the total of previous payments. Payment is made within three weeks of the *Service Manager*'s certificate.

90.5 After a termination certificate has been issued, the *Contractor* does no further work necessary to Provide the Service.

Reasons for termination 91

91.1 Either Party may terminate if the other Party has done one of the following or its equivalent.

- If the other Party is an individual and has

  - presented his petition for bankruptcy (R1),
  - had a bankruptcy order made against him (R2),
  - had a receiver appointed over his assets (R3) or
  - made an arrangement with his creditors (R4).

- If the other Party is a company or partnership and has

  - had a winding-up order made against it (R5),
  - had a provisional liquidator appointed to it (R6),
  - passed a resolution for winding-up (other than in order to amalgamate or reconstruct) (R7),
  - had an administration order made against it (R8),
  - had a receiver, receiver and manager, or administrative receiver appointed over the whole or a substantial part of its undertaking or assets (R9) or
  - made an arrangement with its creditors (R10).

core clauses

main option clauses

secondary option clauses

contract data

91.2 The *Employer* may terminate if the *Service Manager* has notified that t Contractor has defaulted in one of the following ways and not put the defa right within four weeks of the notification.

- Substantially failed to Provide the Service (R11).
- Not provided a bond or guarantee which this contract requires (R12).
- Appointed a Subcontractor for substantial work before the Serv. Manager has accepted the Subcontractor (R13).

91.3 The *Employer* may terminate if the *Service Manager* has notified that t Contractor has defaulted in one of the following ways and not stopp defaulting within four weeks of the notification.

- Substantially hindered the *Employer* or Others (R14).
- Substantially broken a health or safety regulation (R15).

91.4 The *Contractor* may terminate if the *Employer* has not paid an amount certifi by the *Service Manager* within thirteen weeks of the date of the certifica (R16).

91.5 Either Party may terminate if the Parties have been released under the l from further performance of the whole of this contract (R17).

91.6 If the *Service Manager* has instructed the *Contractor* to stop or not to st any substantial work or all work and an instruction allowing the work to start or start has not been given within thirteen weeks,

- the *Employer* may terminate if the instruction was due to a default by t Contractor (R18),
- the *Contractor* may terminate if the instruction was due to a default the *Employer* (R19) and
- either Party may terminate if the instruction was due to any other reas (R20).

91.7 The *Employer* may terminate if an event which the Parties could not reasc ably prevent has substantially affected the *Contractor*'s work for a continuo period of more than thirteen weeks (R21).

Procedures on termination 92

92.1 On termination, the *Employer* may complete the *service* and may use a Plant and Materials provided by the *Contractor* (P1).

92.2 The procedure on termination also includes one or more of the following set out in the Termination Table.

P2 The *Employer* may instruct the *Contractor* to remove any Equipme Plant and Materials and assign the benefit of any subcontract or oth contract related to performance of this contract to the *Employer*.

P3 The *Employer* may use any Equipment to which the *Contractor* has title complete the *service*. The *Contractor* promptly removes the Equipme when the *Service Manager* notifies him that the *Employer* no long requires it to complete the *service*.

P4 The *Contractor* provides to the *Employer* information and other thin which the Service Information states he is to provide at the end of t *service period*.

Payment on termination **93**

93.1   The amount due on termination includes (A1)

- an amount due assessed as for normal payments,
- the Defined Cost for Plant and Materials
  - which have been delivered and retained by the *Employer* or
  - which the *Employer* owns and of which the *Contractor* has to accept delivery,
- other Defined Cost reasonably incurred in expectation of completing the whole of the *service* and
- any amounts retained by the *Employer*.

93.2   The amount due on termination also includes one or more of the following as set out in the Termination Table.

A2   The forecast Defined Cost of removing the Equipment.

A3   A deduction of the forecast of the additional cost to the *Employer* of completing the whole of the *service*.

A4   The *direct fee percentage* applied to

- for Options A and C, any excess of the total of the Prices at the Contract Date over the Price for Services Provided to Date or
- for Option E, any excess of the first forecast of the Defined Cost for the *service* over the Price for Services Provided to Date less the Fee.

21

MAIN OPTION CLAUSES

Option A: Priced contract with price list

<table>
<tr><td>Identified and defined terms</td><td>11</td><td></td></tr>
<tr><td></td><td>11.2</td><td>(17) The Price for Services Provided to Date is the total of</td></tr>
</table>

- the Price for each lump sum item in the Price List which the *Contrac*‌ has completed and
- where a quantity is stated for an item in the Price List, an amount cal‌ lated by multiplying the quantity which the *Contractor* has completed the rate.

(19) The Prices are the amounts stated in the Price column of the Price L‌ Where a quantity is stated for an item in the Price List, the Price is calculat‌ by multiplying the quantity by the rate.

Providing the Service 20

20.5 The *Contractor* prepares forecasts of the final total of the Prices for the wh‌ of the *service* in consultation with the *Service Manager* and submits them the *Service Manager*. Forecasts are prepared at the intervals stated in t‌ Contract Data from the *starting date* until the end of the *service period*. explanation of the changes made since the previous forecast is submitt‌ with each forecast.

The *Contractor*'s plan 21

21.4 The *Contractor* provides information which shows how each item descripti‌ on the Price List relates to the operations on each plan which he submits acceptance.

The Price List 54

54.1 Information in the Price List is not Service Information.

54.2 If the *Contractor* changes a planned method of working at his discretion that the item descriptions on the Price List do not relate to the operations the Accepted Plan, he submits a revision of the Price List to the *Serv*‌ *Manager* for acceptance.

54.3 A reason for not accepting a revision of the Price List is that

- it does not comply with the Accepted Plan,
- any changed Prices are not reasonably distributed between the items the Price List or
- the total of the Prices is changed.

Assessing compensation events 63

63.10 If the effect of a compensation event is to reduce the total Defined Cost a‌ the event is

- a change to the Service Information or
- a correction of an assumption stated by the *Service Manager* for assessi‌ an earlier compensation event,

the Prices are reduced.

63.12 Assessments for changed Prices for compensation events are in the form changes to the Price List.

Implementing	**65**	
compensation events	65.3	The changes to the Price List are included in the notification implementing a compensation event.

core
clauses

main
option clauses

secondary
option clauses

contract
data

Option C: Target contract with price list

Identified and defined terms **11**

11.2 (18) The *Price for Services Provided to Date* is the Defined Cost which *Contractor* has paid plus the Fee.

(20) The Prices are the amounts stated in the Price column of the Price L Where a quantity is stated for an item in the Price List, the Price is calcula by multiplying the quantity by the rate.

Providing the Service **20**

20.3 The *Contractor* advises the *Service Manager* on the practical implications the Accepted Plan and on subcontracting arrangements.

20.4 The *Contractor* prepares forecasts of the total Defined Cost for the whole the *service* in consultation with the *Service Manager* and submits them to *Service Manager*. Forecasts are prepared at the intervals stated in Contract Data from the *starting date* until the end of the *service period*. explanation of the changes made since the previous forecast is submitt with each forecast.

The *Contractor*'s plan **21**

21.4 The *Contractor* provides information which shows how each item descript on the Price List relates to the operations on each plan which he submits acceptance.

Subcontracting **26**

26.4 The *Contractor* submits the proposed contract data for each subcontract acceptance to the *Service Manager* if

- an NEC contract is proposed and
- the *Service Manager* instructs the *Contractor* to make the submission.

A reason for not accepting the proposed contract data is that its use will allow the *Contractor* to Provide the Service.

Tests and inspections **40**

40.7 When the *Service Manager* assesses the cost incurred by the *Employer* repeating a test or inspection after a Defect is found, he does not include t *Contractor*'s cost of carrying out the repeat test or inspection.

Assessing the amount due **50**

50.6 Payments of Defined Cost made by the *Contractor* in a currency other than *currency of this contract* are included in the amount due as payments to made to him in the same currency. Such payments are converted to t *currency of this contract* in order to calculate the Fee and any *Contracto* share using the *exchange rates*.

Defined Cost **52**

52.2 The *Contractor* keeps these records

- accounts of payments of Defined Cost,
- proof that the payments have been made,
- communications about and assessments of compensation events Subcontractors and
- other records as stated in the Service Information.

52.3 The *Contractor* allows the *Service Manager* to inspect at any time with working hours the accounts and records which he is required to keep.

The *Contractor's* share **53**

53.1 The *Service Manager* assesses the *Contractor*'s share of the difference between the total of the Prices and the Price for Services Provided to Date. The difference is divided into increments falling within each of the *share ranges*. The limits of a *share range* are the Price for Services Provided to Date divided by the total of the Prices, expressed as a percentage. The *Contractor*'s share equals the sum of the products of the increment within each *share range* and the corresponding *Contractor's share percentage*.

53.2 If the Price for Services Provided to Date is less than the total of the Prices, the *Contractor* is paid his share of the saving. If the Price for Services Provided to Date is greater than the total of the Prices, the *Contractor* pays his share of the excess.

53.3 At the dates stated in the Contract Data the *Service Manager* assesses the *Contractor*'s share. This share is included in the next amount due following each assessment. The *Service Manager* uses in his assessment the Price for Services Provided to Date and the total of the Prices for the work done at the date of the assessment.

The Price List **54**

54.1 Information in the Price List is not Service Information.

54.2 If the *Contractor* changes a planned method of working at his discretion so that the item descriptions on the Price List do not relate to the operations on the Accepted Plan, he submits a revision of the Price List to the *Service Manager* for acceptance.

54.3 A reason for not accepting a revision of the Price List is that

- it does not comply with the Accepted Plan,
- any changed Prices are not reasonably distributed between the items in the Price List or
- the total of the Prices is changed.

Assessing compensation events **63**

63.11 If the effect of a compensation event is to reduce the total Defined Cost and the event is

- a change to the Service Information, other than a change which the *Contractor* proposed and the *Service Manager* has accepted or
- a correction of an assumption stated by the *Service Manager* for assessing an earlier compensation event,

the Prices are reduced.

63.12 Assessments for changed Prices for compensation events are in the form of changes to the Price List.

Implementing compensation events **65**

65.3 The changes to the Price List are included in the notification implementing a compensation event.

Payment on termination **93**

93.3 If there is a termination, the *Service Manager* assesses the *Contractor*'s share after he has certified termination. His assessment uses, as the Price for Services Provided to Date, the total Defined Cost which the *Contractor* has paid and which he is committed to pay for work done before termination. The assessment uses as the total of the Prices

- the quantity of the work which the *Contractor* has completed for each item on the Price List multiplied by the rate and
- a proportion of each lump sum which is the proportion of the work covered by the item which the *Contractor* has completed.

93.4 The *Service Manager*'s assessment of the *Contractor*'s share is added to the amount due to the *Contractor* on termination if there has been a saving or deducted if there has been an excess.

core clauses

main option clauses

secondary option clauses

contract data

Option E: Cost reimbursable contract

Identified and defined terms	**11** 11.2	(18) The Price for Services Provided to Date is the Defined Cost which t| Contractor has paid plus the Fee.

(21) The Prices are the amounts stated in the Price column of the Price Li:
If no Price List is included, the Prices are the Defined Cost plus the Fee.

Providing the Service **20**

20.3 The Contractor advises the Service Manager on the practical implications
the Accepted Plan and on subcontracting arrangements.

20.4 The Contractor prepares forecasts of the total Defined Cost for the whole
the service in consultation with the Service Manager and submits them to t|
Service Manager. Forecasts are prepared at the intervals stated in t|
Contract Data from the starting date until the end of the service period.
explanation of the changes made since the previous forecast is submitt(
with each forecast.

Subcontracting **26**

26.4 The Contractor submits the proposed contract data for each subcontract f
acceptance to the Service Manager if

- an NEC contract is proposed and
- the Service Manager instructs the Contractor to make the submission.

A reason for not accepting the proposed contract data is that their use will n
allow the Contractor to Provide the Service.

Tests and inspections **40**

40.7 When the Service Manager assesses the cost incurred by the Employer
repeating a test or inspection after a Defect is found, he does not include t|
Contractor's cost of carrying out the repeat test or inspection.

Assessing the amount due **50**

50.7 Payments of Defined Cost made by the Contractor in a currency other than t|
currency of this contract are included in the amount due as payments to |
made to him in the same currency. Such payments are converted to t|
currency of this contract in order to calculate the Fee using the exchang
rates.

Defined Costs **52**

52.2 The Contractor keeps these records

- accounts of payments of Defined Cost,
- proof that the payments have been made,
- communications about and assessments of compensation events f
Subcontractors and
- other records as stated in the Service Information.

52.3 The Contractor allows the Service Manager to inspect at any time with
working hours the accounts and records which he is required to keep.

Implementing compensation events **65**

65.4 The changes to the forecast amount of the Prices are included in the notific
tion implementing a compensation event.

ISPUTE RESOLUTION

ption W1

spute resolution procedure (used **unless United Kingdom Housing Grants, Construction and Regeneration Act** **96 applies**).

Dispute resolution	**W1**	
	W1.1	Any dispute arising under or in connection with this contract is referred to and decided by the *Adjudicator*.
The *Adjudicator*	W1.2	(1) The Parties appoint the *Adjudicator* under the NEC Adjudicator's Contract current at the *starting date*.

(2) The *Adjudicator* acts impartially and decides the dispute as an independent adjudicator and not as an arbitrator.

(3) If the *Adjudicator* is not identified in the Contract Data or if the *Adjudicator* resigns or is unable to act, the Parties choose a new adjudicator jointly. If the Parties have not chosen an adjudicator, either Party may ask the *Adjudicator nominating body* to choose one. The *Adjudicator nominating body* chooses an adjudicator within four days of the request. The chosen adjudicator becomes the *Adjudicator.*

(4) A replacement *Adjudicator* has the power to decide a dispute referred to his predecessor but not decided at the time when the predecessor resigned or became unable to act. He deals with an undecided dispute as if it had been referred to him on the date he was appointed.

(5) The *Adjudicator*, his employees and agents are not liable to the Parties for any action or failure to take action in an adjudication unless the action or failure to take action was in bad faith.

The adjudication W1.3 (1) Disputes are notified and referred to the *Adjudicator* in accordance with the Adjudication Table.

core
clauses

main
option clauses

secondary
option clauses

contract
data

© copyright nec 2005

ADJUDICATION TABLE

Dispute about	Which Party may refer it to the *Adjudicator*?	When may it be referred to the *Adjudicator*?
An action of the *Service Manager*	The *Contractor*	Between two and four weeks after the *Contractor*'s notification of the dispute to the *Employer* and the *Service Manager*, the notification itself being made not more than four weeks after the *Contractor* becomes aware of the action
The *Service Manager* not having taken an action	The *Contractor*	Between two and four weeks after the *Contractor*'s notification of the dispute to the *Employer* and the *Service Manager*, the notification itself being made not more than four weeks after the *Contractor* becomes aware that the action was not taken
A quotation for a compensation event which is treated as having been accepted	The *Employer*	Between two and four weeks after the *Service Manager*'s notification of the dispute to the *Employer* and the *Contractor*, the notification itself being made not more than four weeks after the quotation was treated as accepted
Any other matter	Either Party	Between two and four weeks after notification of the dispute to the other Party and the *Service Manager*

(2) The times for notifying and referring a dispute may be extended by the *Service Manager* if the *Contractor* and the *Service Manager* agree to the extension before the notice or referral is due. The *Service Manager* notifies the extension that has been agreed to the *Contractor*. If a disputed matter is not notified and referred within the times set out in this contract, neither Party may subsequently refer it to the *Adjudicator* or the *tribunal*.

(3) The Party referring the dispute to the *Adjudicator* includes with his referral information to be considered by the *Adjudicator*. Any more information from a Party to be considered by the *Adjudicator* is provided within four weeks of the referral. This period may be extended if the *Adjudicator* and the Parties agree.

(4) If a matter disputed by the *Contractor* under or in connection with a subcontract is also a matter disputed under or in connection with this contract and if the subcontract allows, the *Contractor* may refer the subcontract dispute to the *Adjudicator* at the same time as the main contract referral. The *Adjudicator* then decides on the disputes together and references to the Parties for the purposes of the dispute are interpreted as including the Subcontractor.

(5) The *Adjudicator* may

- review and revise any action or inaction of the *Service Manager* related to the dispute and alter a quotation which has been treated as having been accepted,
- take the initiative in ascertaining the facts and the law related to the dispute,
- instruct a Party to provide further information related to the dispute within a stated time and
- instruct a Party to take any other action which he considers necessary to reach his decision and to do so within a stated time.

(6) A communication between a Party and the *Adjudicator* is communicated to the other Party at the same time.

(7) If the *Adjudicator's* decision includes assessment of additional cost or delay caused to the *Contractor*, he makes his assessment in the same way as a compensation event is assessed.

(8) The *Adjudicator* decides the dispute and notifies the Parties and the *Service Manager* of his decision and his reasons within four weeks of the end of the period for receiving information. This four week period may be extended if the Parties agree.

(9) Unless and until the *Adjudicator* has notified the Parties of his decision, the Parties and the *Service Manager* proceed as if the matter disputed was not disputed.

(10) The *Adjudicator's* decision is binding on the Parties unless and until revised by the *tribunal* and is enforceable as a matter of contractual obligation between the Parties and not as an arbitral award. The *Adjudicator's* decision is final and binding if neither Party has notified the other within the times required by this contract that he is dissatisfied with a decision of the *Adjudicator* and intends to refer the matter to the *tribunal*.

(11) The *Adjudicator* may, within two weeks of giving his decision to the Parties, correct any clerical mistake or ambiguity.

Review by the *tribunal*   W1.4   (1) A Party does not refer any dispute under or in connection with this contract to the *tribunal* unless it has first been referred to the *Adjudicator* in accordance with this contract.

(2) If, after the *Adjudicator* notifies his decision a Party is dissatisfied, he may notify the other Party that he intends to refer it to the *tribunal*. A Party may not refer a dispute to the *tribunal* unless this notification is given within four weeks of notification of the *Adjudicator's* decision.

(3) If the *Adjudicator* does not notify his decision within the time provided by this contract, a Party may notify the other Party that he intends to refer the dispute to the *tribunal*. A Party may not refer a dispute to the *tribunal* unless this notification is given within four weeks of the date by which the *Adjudicator* should have notified his decision.

(4) The *tribunal* settles the dispute referred to it. The *tribunal* has the powers to reconsider any decision of the *Adjudicator* and review and revise any action or inaction of the *Service Manager* related to the dispute. A Party is not limited in the *tribunal* proceedings to the information, evidence or arguments put to the *Adjudicator*.

(5) If the *tribunal* is arbitration, the arbitration procedure, the place where the arbitration is to be held and the method of choosing the arbitrator are those stated in the Contract Data.

(6) A Party does not call the *Adjudicator* as a witness in *tribunal* proceedings.

core
clauses

main
option clauses

secondary
option clauses

contract
data

Option W2

Dispute resolution procedure (used in the United Kingdom when the Housing Grants, Construction and Regenerat Act 1996 applies).

Dispute resolution W2

W2.1 (1) Any dispute arising under or in connection with this contract is referrec and decided by the *Adjudicator*. A Party may refer a dispute to the *Adjudica* at any time.

(2) In this Option, time periods stated in days exclude Christmas Day, Gc Friday and bank holidays.

The *Adjudicator* W2.2

(1) The Parties appoint the *Adjudicator* under the NEC Adjudicator's Contr current at the *starting date*.

(2) The *Adjudicator* acts impartially and decides the dispute as an indep dent adjudicator and not as an arbitrator.

(3) If the *Adjudicator* is not identified in the Contract Data or if the *Adjudica* resigns or becomes unable to act

- the Parties may choose an adjudicator jointly or
- a Party may ask the *Adjudicator nominating body* to choose an adju cator.

The *Adjudicator nominating body* chooses an adjudicator within four days the request. The chosen adjudicator becomes the *Adjudicator*.

(4) A replacement *Adjudicator* has the power to decide a dispute referred his predecessor but not decided at the time when his predecessor resigned became unable to act. He deals with an undecided dispute as if it had be referred to him on the date he was appointed.

(5) The *Adjudicator,* his employees and agents are not liable to the Parties any action or failure to take action in an adjudication unless the action failure to take action was in bad faith.

The adjudication W2.3

(1) Before a Party refers a dispute to the *Adjudicator*, he gives a notice adjudication to the other Party with a brief description of the dispute and t decision which he wishes the *Adjudicator* to make. If the *Adjudicator* is nam in the Contract Data, the Party sends a copy of the notice of adjudication the *Adjudicator* when it is issued. Within three days of the receipt of the noti of adjudication, the *Adjudicator* notifies the Parties

- that he is able to decide the dispute in accordance with the contract or
- that he is unable to decide the dispute and has resigned.

If the *Adjudicator* does not so notify within three days of the issue of t notice of adjudication, either Party may act as if he has resigned.

(2) Within seven days of a Party giving a notice of adjudication he

- refers the dispute to the *Adjudicator*,
- provides the *Adjudicator* with the information on which he relies, includi any supporting documents and
- provides a copy of the information and supporting documents he h provided to the *Adjudicator* to the other Party.

core clauses

main option clauses

secondary option clauses

contract data

Any further information from a Party to be considered by the *Adjudicator* is provided within fourteen days of the referral. This period may be extended if the *Adjudicator* and the Parties agree.

(3) If a matter disputed by the *Contractor* under or in connection with a subcontract is also a matter disputed under or in connection with this contract, the *Contractor* may, with the consent of the Subcontractor, refer the subcontract dispute to the *Adjudicator* at the same time as the main contract referral. The *Adjudicator* then decides the disputes together and references to the Parties for the purposes of the dispute are interpreted as including the Subcontractor.

(4) The *Adjudicator* may

- review and revise any action or inaction of the *Service Manager* related to the dispute and alter a quotation which has been treated as having been accepted,
- take the initiative in ascertaining the facts and the law related to the dispute,
- instruct a Party to provide further information related to the dispute within a stated time and
- instruct a Party to take any other action which he considers necessary to reach his decision and to do so within a stated time.

(5) If a Party does not comply with any instruction within the time stated by the *Adjudicator,* the *Adjudicator* may continue the adjudication and make his decision based upon the information and evidence he has received.

(6) A communication between a Party and the *Adjudicator* is communicated to the other Party at the same time.

(7) If the *Adjudicator's* decision includes assessment of additional cost or delay caused to the *Contractor,* he makes his assessment in the same way as a compensation event is assessed.

(8) The *Adjudicator* decides the dispute and notifies the Parties and the *Service Manager* of his decision and his reasons within twenty-eight days of the dispute being referred to him. This period may be extended by up to fourteen days with the consent of the referring Party or by any other period agreed by the Parties.

(9) Unless and until the Adjudicator has notified the Parties of his decision, the Parties and the *Service Manager* proceed as if the matter disputed was not disputed.

(10) If the *Adjudicator* does not make his decision and notify it to the Parties within the time provided by this contract, the Parties and the *Adjudicator* may agree to extend the period for making his decision. If they do not agree to an extension, either Party may act as if the *Adjudicator* has resigned.

(11) The *Adjudicator's* decision is binding on the Parties unless and until revised by the *tribunal* and is enforceable as a matter of contractual obligation between the Parties and not as an arbitral award. The *Adjudicator's* decision is final and binding if neither Party has notified the other within the times required by this contract that he is dissatisfied with a matter decided by the *Adjudicator* and intends to refer the matter to the *tribunal*.

(12) The *Adjudicator* may, within fourteen days of giving his decision to the Parties, correct a clerical mistake or ambiguity.

core
clauses

main
option clauses

secondary
option clauses

contract
data

Review by the *tribunal* W2.4 (1) A Party does not refer any dispute under or in connection with contract to the *tribunal* unless it has first been decided by the *Adjudicatc* accordance with this contract.

(2) If, after the *Adjudicator* notifies his decision a Party is dissatisfied, Party may notify the other Party of the matter which he disputes and state he intends to refer it to the *tribunal*. The dispute may not be referred to *tribunal* unless this notification is given within four weeks of the notificatio the *Adjudicator's* decision.

(3) The *tribunal* settles the dispute referred to it. The *tribunal* has the pov to reconsider any decision of the *Adjudicator* and to review and revise action or inaction of the *Service Manager* related to the dispute. A Part not limited in *tribunal* proceedings to the information or evidence put to *Adjudicator*.

(4) If the *tribunal* is arbitration, the *arbitration procedure,* the place where arbitration is to be held and the method of choosing the arbitrator are th stated in the Contract Data.

(5) A Party does not call the *Adjudicator* as a witness in *tribunal* proceedin

tion X1: Price adjustment for inflation (used only with Options A and C)

Defined terms **X1**

X1.1 (a) The Base Date Index (B) is the latest available index before the *base date*.

(b) The Latest Index (L) is the latest available index before the date of assessment of an amount due.

(c) The Price Adjustment Factor is the total of the products of each of the proportions stated in the Contract Data multiplied by $(L - B)/B$ for the index linked to it.

Price Adjustment Factor X1.2 If an index is changed after it has been used in calculating a Price Adjustment Factor, the calculation is repeated and a correction included in the next assessment of the amount due.

Compensation events X1.3 The Defined Cost for compensation events is assessed using the

- Defined Cost current at the time of assessing the compensation event adjusted to *base date* by dividing by one plus the Price Adjustment Factor for the last assessment of the amount due and
- Defined Cost at *base date* levels for amounts calculated from rates and prices in the Price List.

Price adjustment X1.4 Each amount due includes an amount for price adjustment which is the sum of
Option A

- the change in the Price for Services Provided to Date since the last assessment of the amount due multiplied by the Price Adjustment Factor for the date of the current assessment,
- the amount for price adjustment included in the previous amount due and
- correcting amounts, not included elsewhere, which arise from changes to indices used for assessing previous amounts for price adjustment.

Price adjustment X1.5 Each time the amount due is assessed, an amount for price adjustment is
Option C added to the total of the Prices which is the sum of

- the change in the Price for Services Provided to Date since the last assessment of the amount due multiplied by $(PAF/(1 + PAF))$ where PAF is the Price Adjustment Factor for the date of the current assessment and
- correcting amounts, not included elsewhere, which arise from changes to indices used for assessing previous amounts for price adjustment.

core clauses

main option clauses

secondary option clauses

contract data

33

Option X2: Changes in the law

Changes in the law   X2

X2.1   A change in the law of the country in which the Affected Property is loca is a compensation event if it occurs after the Contract Date. The *Serv Manager* may notify the *Contractor* of a compensation event for a change the law and instruct him to submit quotations. If the effect of a compensati event which is a change in the law is to reduce the total Defined Cost, Prices are reduced.

Option X3: Multiple currencies (used only with Option A)

Multiple currencies   X3

X3.1   The *Contractor* is paid in currencies other than the *currency of this contract* the items or activities listed in the Contract Data. The *exchange rates* used to convert from the *currency of this contract* to other currencies.

X3.2   Payments to the *Contractor* in currencies other than the *currency of t contract* do not exceed the maximum amounts stated in the Contract Da Any excess is paid in the *currency of this contract*.

Option X4: Parent company guarantee

Parent company   X4
guarantee   X4.1   If a parent company owns the *Contractor*, the *Contractor* gives to the *Emplo* a guarantee by the parent company of the *Contractor*'s performance in t form set out in the Service Information. If the guarantee was not given by t Contract Date, it is given to the *Employer* within four weeks of the Contr Date.

Option X12: Partnering

Identified and defined   X12
terms   X12.1   (1) The Partners are those named in the Schedule of Partners. The *Client* is Partner.

(2) An Own Contract is a contract between two Partners which includes t Option.

(3) The Core Group comprises the Partners listed in the Schedule of Cc Group Members.

(4) Partnering Information is information which specifies how the Partne work together and is either in the documents which the Contract Data stat it is in or in an instruction given in accordance with this contract.

(5) A Key Performance Indicator is an aspect of performance for which target is stated in the Schedule of Partners.

Actions X12.2 (1) Each Partner works with the other Partners to achieve the *Client's objective* stated in the Contract Data and the objectives of every other Partner stated in the Schedule of Partners.

(2) Each Partner nominates a representative to act for him in dealings with other Partners.

(3) The Core Group acts and takes decisions on behalf of the Partners on those matters stated in the Partnering Information.

(4) The Partners select the members of the Core Group. The Core Group decides how they will work and decides the dates when each member joins and leaves the Core Group. The *Client's* representative leads the Core Group unless stated otherwise in the Partnering Information.

(5) The Core Group keeps the Schedule of Core Group Members and the Schedule of Partners up to date and issues copies of them to the Partners each time either is revised.

(6) This Option does not create a legal partnership between Partners who are not one of the Parties in this contract.

Working together X12.3 (1) The Partners work together as stated in the Partnering Information and in a spirit of mutual trust and co-operation.

(2) A Partner may ask another Partner to provide information which he needs to carry out the work in his Own Contract and the other Partner provides it.

(3) Each Partner gives an early warning to the other Partners when he becomes aware of any matter that could affect the achievement of another Partner's objectives stated in the Schedule of Partners.

(4) The Partners use common information systems as set out in the Partnering Information.

(5) A Partner implements a decision of the Core Group by issuing instructions in accordance with its Own Contracts.

(6) The Core Group may give an instruction to the Partners to change the Partnering Information. Each such change to the Partnering Information is a compensation event which may lead to reduced Prices.

(7) The Core Group prepares and maintains a timetable showing the proposed timing of the contributions of the Partners. The Core Group issues a copy of the timetable to the Partners each time it is revised. The *Contractor* changes his plan if it is necessary to do so in order to comply with the revised time-table. Each such change is a compensation event which may lead to reduced Prices.

(8) A Partner gives advice, information and opinion to the Core Group and to other Partners when asked to do so by the Core Group. This advice, information and opinion relates to work that another Partner is to carry out under its Own Contract and is given fully, openly and objectively. The Partners show contingency and risk allowances in information about costs, prices and timing for future work.

(9) A Partner notifies the Core Group before subcontracting any work.

Incentives X12.4 (1) A Partner is paid the amount stated in the Schedule of Partners if the target stated for a Key Performance Indicator is improved upon or achieved. Payment of the amount is due when the target has been improved upon or achieved and is made as part of the amount due in the Partner's Own Contract.

(2) The *Client* may add a Key Performance Indicator and associated payment to the Schedule of Partners but may not delete or reduce a payment stated in the Schedule of Partners.

core clauses

main option clauses

secondary option clauses

contract data

Option X13: Performance bond

Performance bond **X13**

X13.1 The *Contractor* gives the *Employer* a performance bond, provided by a bank ⌐ insurer which the *Service Manager* has accepted, for the amount stated in th⌐ Contract Data and in the form set out in the Service Information. A reason f⌐ not accepting the bank or insurer is that its commercial position is not stro⌐ enough to carry the bond. If the bond was not given by the Contract Date, it ⌐ given to the *Employer* within four weeks of the Contract Date.

Option X17: Low service damages

Low service damages **X17**

X17.1 If a part of the *service* does not meet the service level stated in the *servic⌐ level table*, the *Contractor* pays the amount of low service damages stated ⌐ the *service level table*.

Option X18: Limitation of liability

Limitation of liability **X18**

X18.1 The *Contractor*'s liability to the *Employer* for the *Employer*'s indirect or cons⌐ quential loss is limited to the amount stated in the Contract Data.

X18.2 For any one event, the liability of the *Contractor* to the *Employer* for loss of ⌐ damage to the *Employer*'s property is limited to the amount stated in th⌐ Contract Data.

X18.3 The *Contractor*'s liability to the *Employer* for Defects due to his design of ⌐ item of Equipment is limited to the amount stated in the Contract Data.

X18.4 The *Contractor*'s total liability to the *Employer* for all matters arising under ⌐ in connection with this contract, other than the excluded matters, is limited ⌐ the amount stated in the Contract Data and applies in contract, tort or deli⌐ and otherwise to the extent allowed under the *law of the contract*.

The excluded matters are amounts payable by the *Contractor* as stated in th⌐ contract for

- loss of or damage to the *Employer's* property,
- low service damages if Option X17 applies,
- delay damages if Option X19 applies and
- *Contractor*'s share if Option C applies.

X18.5 The *Contractor* is not liable to the *Employer* for a matter unless it is notified ⌐ the *Contractor* before the *end of liability date*.

core clauses

main option clauses

secondary option clauses

contract data

tion X19: Task Order

Identified and defined **X19**
terms X19.1 (1) A Task is work within the *service* which the *Service Manager* may instruct the *Contractor* to carry out within a stated period of time.

(2) A Task Order is the *Service Manager*'s instruction to carry out a Task.

(3) Task Completion is when the *Contractor* has done all the work in the Task and corrected Defects which would have prevented the *Employer* or Others from using the Affected Property and Others from doing their work.

(4) Task Completion Date is the date for completion stated in the Task Order unless later changed in accordance with this contract.

Providing the Service X19.2 A Task Order includes

- a detailed description of the work in the Task,
- a priced list of items of work in the Task in which items taken from the Price List are identified,
- the starting and completion dates for the Task,
- the amount of delay damages for the late completion of the Task and
- the total of the Prices for the Task when Option A or C is used or the forecast total of the Prices for the Task if Option E is used.

The *Service Manager* consults the *Contractor* about the contents of a Task Order before he issues it.

X19.3 The delay damages in a Task Order, if any, are not more than the estimated cost to the *Employer* of late completion of the Task. If Task Completion is later than the Task Completion Date, the *Contractor* pays delay damages at the rate stated in the Task Order from the Task Completion Date until Task Completion.

The Prices for items in the Task price list which are not taken from the Price List are assessed in the same way as compensation events.

Time X19.4 The *Contractor* does not start any work included in the Task until the *Service Manager* has instructed him to carry out the Task and does the work so that Task Completion is on or before the Task Completion Date. No Task Order is issued after the end of the *service period*.

Task Order programme X19.5 The *Contractor* submits a Task Order programme to the *Service Manager* for acceptance within the period stated in the Contract Data.

core
clauses

main
option clauses

secondary
option clauses

contract
data

X19.6 The *Contractor* shows on each Task Order programme which he submits acceptance

- the Task starting date and the Task Completion Date,
- planned Task Completion,
- the order and timing of the operations which the *Contractor* plans to in order to complete the Task,
- provisions for

  - float,
  - time risk allowances,
  - health and safety requirements and
  - the procedures set out in this contract,

- the dates when, in order to Provide the Service in accordance with Task Order programme, the *Contractor* will need

  - access to the Affected Property,
  - acceptances,
  - Plant and Materials, equipment and other things to be provided by *Employer* and
  - information from Others,

- for each operation, a statement of how the *Contractor* plans to do work identifying the principal Equipment and other resources which plans to use and
- other information which the Service Information requires the *Contrac* to show on a Task Order programme submitted for acceptance.

X19.7 Within one week of the *Contractor* submitting a Task Order programme to h for acceptance, the *Service Manager* either accepts the programme or notifi the *Contractor* of his reasons for not accepting it. A reason for not accept the Task Order programme is that

- the *Contractor*'s plans which it shows are not practicable,
- it does not show the information which this contract requires or
- it does not comply with the Service Information.

Revising the Task Order programme

X19.8 The *Contractor* shows on each revised Task Order programme

- the actual progress achieved on each operation and its effect upon t timing of the remaining work,
- the effects of implemented compensation events,
- how the *Contractor* plans to deal with any delays and to correct notifi Defects and
- any other changes which the *Contractor* proposes to make to the Ta Order programme.

X19.9 The *Contractor* submits a revised Task Order programme to the *Serv Manager* for acceptance

- within the *period for reply* after the *Service Manager* has instructed h to and
- when the *Contractor* chooses to.

The latest programme accepted by the *Service Manager* supersedes previo accepted programmes.

Compensation events

X19.10 The following are compensation events.

(1) The *Service Manager* gives an instruction changing a Task Order.

(2) The *Contractor* receives the Task Order after the starting date stated the Task Order.

(3) The *Employer* does not provide the right of access to the Affected Prope in accordance with the latest accepted Task Order programme.

(4) The *Employer* does not provide something which he is to provide as stated in the Service Information in accordance with the latest accepted Task Order programme.

(5) The *Employer* or Others do not work in accordance with the latest accepted Task Order programme or within the conditions stated in the Service Information.

(6) An event which

- stops the *Contractor* completing a Task or
- stops the *Contractor* completing a Task by the Task Completion Date,

and which

- neither Party could prevent,
- an experienced contractor would have judged at the date of issue of the Task Order to have such a small chance of occurring that it would have been unreasonable for him to have allowed for it and
- is not one of the other compensation events stated in this contract.

(7) A Task Completion Date is later than the end of the *service period*.

X19.11 If, due to the compensation event, planned Task Completion is delayed, the delay is stated in the *Contractor*'s quotation for the event and a programme is submitted with details of the assessment of the delay.

Assessments of delay include time risk allowances and are based on the assumption that the Task Order programme can be changed and that delays were or will be reasonably incurred.

The *Service Manager* may assess the delay if, when the *Contractor* submits quotations for a compensation event, the *Contractor* has not submitted a Task Order programme required by this contract.

Implementing compensation events X19.12 The changes to the calculated total of the Prices for the Task Order and any delay to the Task Completion Date are included in the *Service Manager*'s notification implementing a compensation event.

ption X20: Key Performance Indicators (not used with Option X12)

Incentives X20

X20.1 A Key Performance Indicator is an aspect of performance by the *Contractor* for which a target is stated in the Incentive Schedule. The Incentive Schedule is the *incentive schedule* unless later changed in accordance with this contract.

X20.2 From the *starting date* until the end of the *service period*, the *Contractor* reports to the *Service Manager* his performance against each of the Key Performance Indicators. Reports are provided at the intervals stated in the Contract Data and include the forecast final measurement against each indicator.

X20.3 If the *Contractor*'s forecast final measurement against a Key Performance Indicator will not achieve the target stated in the Incentive Schedule, he submits to the *Service Manager* his proposals for improving performance.

X20.4 The *Contractor* is paid the amount stated in the Incentive Schedule if the target stated for a Key Performance Indicator is improved upon or achieved. Payment of the amount is due when the target has been improved upon or achieved.

X20.5 The *Employer* may add a Key Performance Indicator and associated payment to the Incentive Schedule but may not delete or reduce a payment stated in the Incentive Schedule.

Option Y

Option Y(UK)2: The Housing Grants, Construction and Regeneration Act 1996

Definitions Y(UK)2

Y2.1 (1) The Act is The Housing Grants, Construction and Regeneration Act 199(

(2) A period of time stated in days is a period calculated in accordance w Section 116 of the Act.

Dates for payment Y2.2 The date on which a payment becomes due is seven days after the asse⸱ment date.

The final date for payment is fourteen days or a different period for paymen¹ stated in the Contract Data after the date on which payment becomes due.

The *Service Manager's* certificate is the notice of payment from the *Emplo*⸱ to the *Contractor* specifying the amount of the payment made or proposed be made and stating how the amount was calculated.

Notice of intention to Y2.3 If either Party intends to withhold payment of an amount due under t⸱
withhold payment contract, he notifies the other Party not later than seven days (the prescrib⸱ period) before the final date for payment by stating the amount proposed be withheld and the reason for withholding payment. If there is more than o⸱ reason, the amount for each reason is stated.

A Party does not withhold payment of an amount due under this contra⸱ unless he has notified his intention to withhold payment as required by t⸱ contract.

Suspension of Y2.4 If the *Contractor* exercises his right under the Act to suspend performance it⸱
performance a compensation event.

Option Y(UK)3: The Contracts (Rights of Third Parties) Act 1999

Third party rights Y(UK)3

Y3.1 A person or organisation who is not one of the Parties may enforce a term this contract under the Contracts (Rights of Third Parties) Act 1999 only⸱ the term and the person or organisation are stated in the Contract Data.

Option Z: *Additional conditions of contract*

Additional conditions of Z1
contract Z1.1 The *additional conditions of contract* stated in the Contract Data are part this contract.

Sidebar: core clauses / main option clauses / secondary option clauses / contract data

rt one – Data provided by the *Employer*

Completion of the data in full, according to the Options chosen, is essential to create a complete contract.

Statements given in all contracts

1 General

- The *conditions of contract* are the core clauses and the clauses for main Option ....., dispute resolution Option ..... and secondary Options ..... of the NEC3 Term Service Contract June 2005 (with amendments June 2006).

- The *service* is . . . .

- The *Employer* is

  Name . . . .

  Address . . . .

  . . . .

- The *Service Manager* is

  Name . . . .

  Address . . . .

  . . . .

- The *Adjudicator* is

  Name . . . .

  Address . . . .

  . . . .

- The Affected Property is

  . . . .

  . . . .

  . . . .

- The Service Information is in

  . . . .

  . . . .

  . . . .

- The *language of this contract* is . . . .

- The *law of the contract* is the law of . . . .

- The *period for reply* is . . . . weeks.

- The *Adjudicator nominating body* is . . . .

- The *tribunal* is . . . .

core clauses

main option clauses

secondary option clauses

contract data

© copyright nec 2005   41

• The following matters will be included in the Risk Register

....
....
....

3 Time

• The *starting date* is ....
• The *service period* is ....

5 Payment

• The *assessment interval* is .... weeks (not more than fi
• The *currency of this contract* is the ....
• The *interest rate* is ......% per annum (not less than 2) above the ....
.... rate of the .... ba

8 Risks and insurance

• The minimum amount of cover for insurance against loss of or dama
  caused by the *Contractor* to the *Employer*'s property is ....
• The minimum amount of cover for insurance in respect of loss of or dama
  to property (except the *Employer*'s property, Plant and Materials and Equ
  ment) and liability for bodily injury to or death of a person (not an employ
  of the *Contractor*) arising from or in connection with the *Contracto*
  Providing the Service for any one event is ....
• The minimum limit of indemnity for insurance in respect of death of
  bodily injury to employees of the *Contractor* arising out of and in t
  course of their employment in connection with this contract for any o
  event is ....

Optional statements

If the *tribunal* is arbitration

• The *arbitration procedure* is ....
• The place where the arbitration is to be held is...................
• The person or organisation who will choose an arbitrator
    • if the Parties cannot agree a choice or
    • if the *arbitration procedure* does not state who selects an arbitrator i
  ....

If no plan is identified in part two of the Contract Data

• The *Contractor* submits a first plan for acceptance within.......... wee
  of the Contract Date.

**If the period in which payments are made is not three weeks and Y(UK)2
not used**

• The period within which payments are made is ....

**If Y(UK)2 is used and the final date for payment is not 14 days after the da
when payment is due**

• The period for payment is ....

If there are additional *Employer*'s risks

- These are additional *Employer*'s risks

    1 ....

    2 ....

    3 ....

If the *Employer* is to provide Plant and Materials

- The insurance against loss of or damage to Plant and Materials is to include cover for Plant and Materials provided by the *Employer* for an amount of ....

If the *Employer* is to provide any of the insurances stated in the Insurance Table

- The *Employer* provides these insurances from the Insurance Table

    1. Insurance against..

    Cover/indemnity is ....

    The deductibles are..

    2. Insurance against..

    Cover/indemnity is ....

    The deductibles are..

    3. Insurance against..

    Cover/indemnity is ....

    The deductibles are..

If additional insurances are to be provided

- The *Employer* provides these additional insurances

    1. Insurance against..

    Cover/indemnity is ....

    The deductibles are..

    2. Insurance against..

    Cover/indemnity is ....

    The deductibles are..

- The *Contractor* provides these additional insurances

    1. Insurance against..

    Cover/indemnity is ....

    The deductibles are..

    2. Insurance against..

    Cover/indemnity is ....

    The deductibles are..

core clauses

main option clauses

secondary option clauses

contract data

If Option A is used

- The *Contractor* prepares forecasts of the final total of the Prices for the whole of the *service* at intervals no longer than . . . . wee

If Option C is used

- The *Contractor's share percentages* and the *share ranges* are

share range	Contractor's share percentage
less than . . . . %	. . . .
from . . . . % to . . . . %	. . . .
from . . . . % to . . . . %	. . . .
greater than . . . . %	. . . .

- The *Contractor*'s share is assessed on (dates)

. . . .
. . . .
. . . .
. . . .

If Option C or E is used

- The *Contractor* prepares forecasts of the total Defined Cost for the whole the *service* at intervals no longer than . . . . wee
- The *exchange rates* are those published in . . . . on . . . . (dat

If Option X1 is used

- The proportions used to calculate the Price Adjustment Factor are

0. . . . . linked to the index for	
0.	. . . .
0.	. . . .
0.	. . . .
0.	. . . .
0.	. . . .
0. . . . . non-adjustable	

1.00

- The *base date* for indices is . . . .
- The indices are those prepared by. . . . .

If Option X3 is used

- The *Employer* will pay for the items or activities listed below in the currenci stated

items and activities	other currency	total maximum payme in the currency
. . . .	. . . .	. . . .
. . . .	. . . .	. . . .
. . . .	. . . .	. . . .
. . . .	. . . .	. . . .

- The *exchange rates* are those published in . . . .
  on . . . . (date).

If Option X12 is used

- The *Client* is
  Name . . . .
  Address . . . .
  . . . .

- The *Client's objective* is
  . . . .
  . . . .
  . . . .
  . . . .
  . . . .
  . . . .

- The Partnering Information is in
  . . . .
  . . . .
  . . . .
  . . . .
  . . . .

If Option X13 is used

- The amount of the performance bond is . . . .

If Option X17 is used

- The *service level table* is . . . .

If Option X18 is used

- The *Contractor's* liability to the *Employer* for indirect or consequential loss is
  limited to
  . . . .

- For any one event, the *Contractor's* liability to the *Employer* for loss of or
  damage to the *Employer's* property is limited to . . . .

- The *Contractor's* liability for Defects due to his design of an item of
  Equipment is limited to . . . .

- The *Contractor's* total liability to the *Employer* for all matters arising under
  or in connection with this contract, other than the excluded matters, is
  limited to . . . .

- The *end of liability date* is . . . . years after the end of the *service period*.

If Option X19 is used

- The *Contractor* submits a Task Order programme to the *Service Manager*
  within . . . . days of receiving the Task Order.

core clauses

main
option clauses

secondary
option clauses

contract
data

If Option X20 is used (but not if Option X12 is also used)

- The *incentive schedule* for Key Performance Indicators is in . . . .

- A report of performance against each Key Performance Indicator is provid
  at intervals of . . . . months.

If Option Y(UK)3 is used

- term   person or organisation

  . . . .

  . . . .

  . . . .

  . . . .

If Option Z is used

- The *additional conditions of contract* are . . . .

  . . . .

Part two – Data provided by the *Contractor*

Completion of the data in full, according to the Options chosen, is essential to create a complete contract.

Statements given in all contracts

- The *Contractor* is

    Name . . . .

    Address . . . .

    . . . .

    . . . .

- The *direct fee percentage* is . . . . %.

- The *subcontracted fee percentage* is . . . . %.

- The key persons are

  (1) Name . . . .

      Job . . . .

      Responsibilities . . . .

      Qualifications . . . .

      Experience . . . .

      . . . .

  (2) Name . . . .

      Job . . . .

      Responsibilities . . . .

      Qualifications . . . .

      Experience . . . .

      . . . .

- The following matters will be included in the Risk Register

  . . . .

  . . . .

  . . . .

Optional statements

If the *Contractor* is to provide Service Information for his plan

- The Service Information for the *Contractor's* plan is in . . . .

If a plan is identified in the Contract Data

- The plan identified in the Contract Data is . . . .

If Option A, C or E is used

- The *price list* is . . . .

If Option A or C is used

- The tendered total of the Prices is . . . .

core clauses

main option clauses

secondary option clauses

contract data

nec®3 Term Service Contract

Index by clause numbers (Option clauses indicated by their letters, main clause heads by bold numbers). Terms in *italics* are identified in Contract Data, and defined terms have capital initial letters.

© copyright nec 2005